Top Gun Of The Sky

By Martin Bradley

Thanks to Ashley Smith and Penny Smout at Hawk Conservancy Trust, Nigel Burt and ExxonMobil at Fawley Refinery, Simon Chadwick, Linda Wright Photography, and not forgetting Claire, Jay and Max.

Ceratopia Books, 2 Solent Road, Dibden Purlieu, SO45 4QG

ISBN 0954279123
Printed by John Dollin Printing Services Ltd, Whitchurch, Hampshire

D0307806

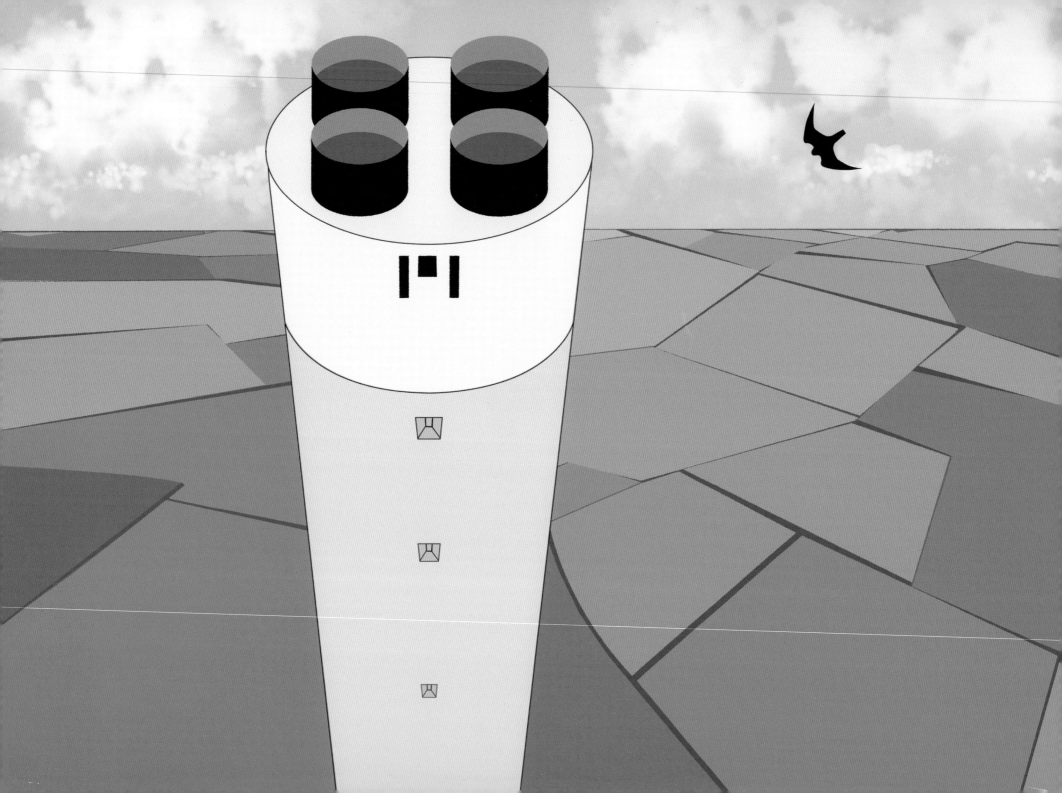

Flick the pages to see the falcon stoop

On top of a chimney 600 feet high,

Is the home of a raptor,
Top Gun of the Sky.

A flying machine designed to attack,

It stoops on its prey
thrusting talons in back.

With streamline body and pointed sails,

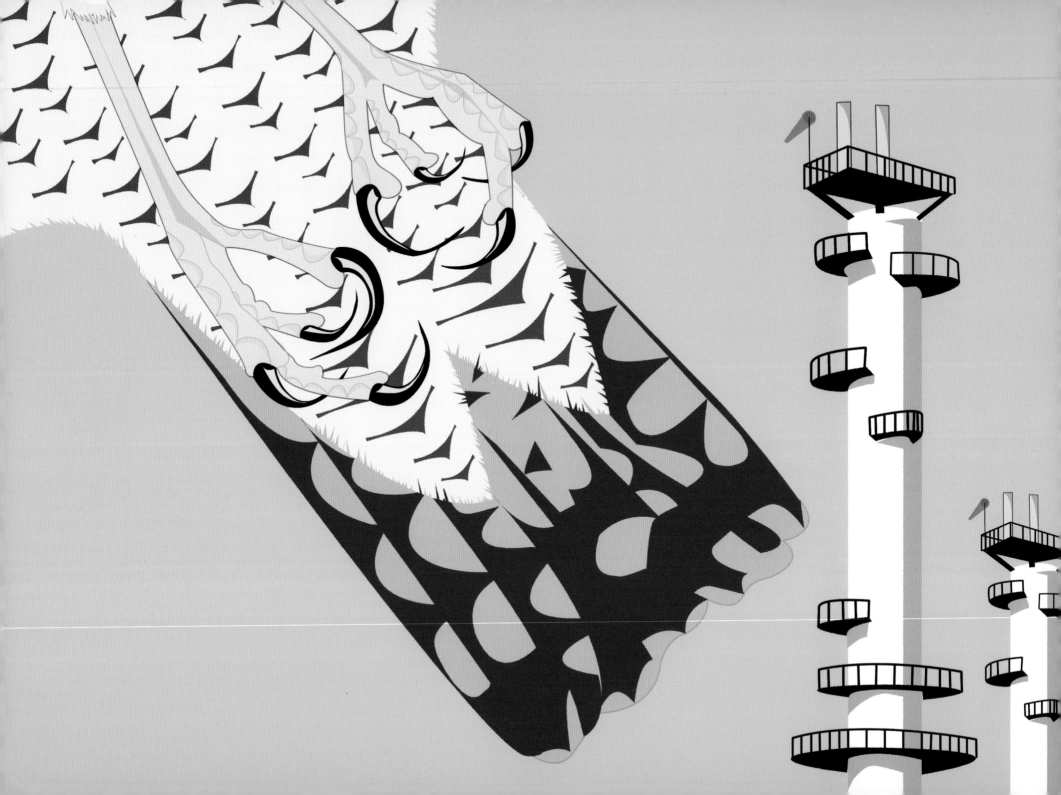

Its deadly weapons carried under its tail.

Floating on thermals, increasing in height.
Quartering circles with effortless flight.

Searching for movement amongst turbulent flow,

A flap of wings, a teardrop, no sound.

Gathering speed, stoops to the ground.

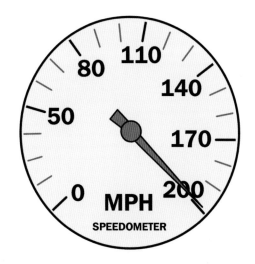

Clean impact of talons, feathers explode,

Race for life over, now carrying load.

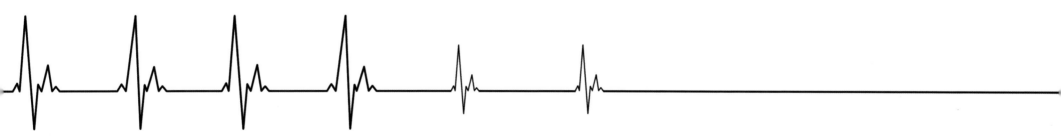

Sharp weapons are clamped on
the chest of deceased.

Hooded head,
hunching shoulders,
concealing from thieves.

Prize taken to nest, young waiting for kill.
Pigeon prepared for the family meal.

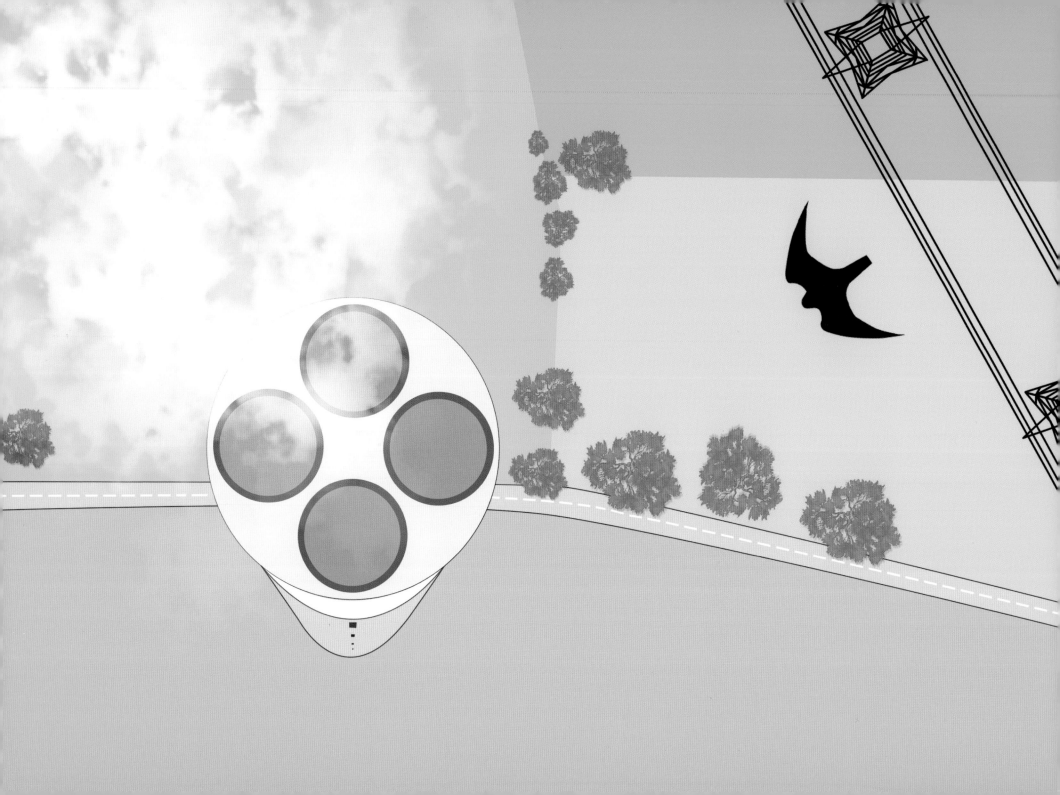

Refuelled, back to safety, 600 feet high.
The Peregrine Falcon,
Top Gun of the Sky.

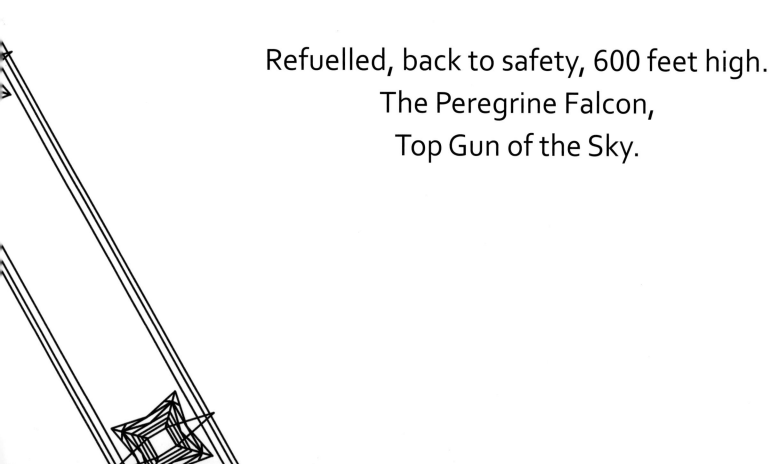

Falconry Terms

Talon
Raptor toenail

Jesses
Leather straps attached to a trained falcon's leg

Hood
A cap covering eyes and head to keep a bird calm. *"Hoodwink"*, *"keep in the dark"* and *"chaperone"* all derive from a falcon wearing a hood

Eyass
Young bird in nest not able to fly

"Worth your weight in gold"
Money paid to falconers or trappers that caught falcons for royalty

Quartering
Slow, low hunting flight

Sails
A falcon's wings

Eyrie
Nesting place of a bird of prey

Stoop
Rapid descent in chase of prey

Lure
Imitation quarry swung on a line

Falconer
A person who flies a falcon

Tomial Tooth
Notch in a falcon's beak

Mantle
To hide food from onlookers with wings and tail

Quarry
Another name for prey

Draw A Peregrine

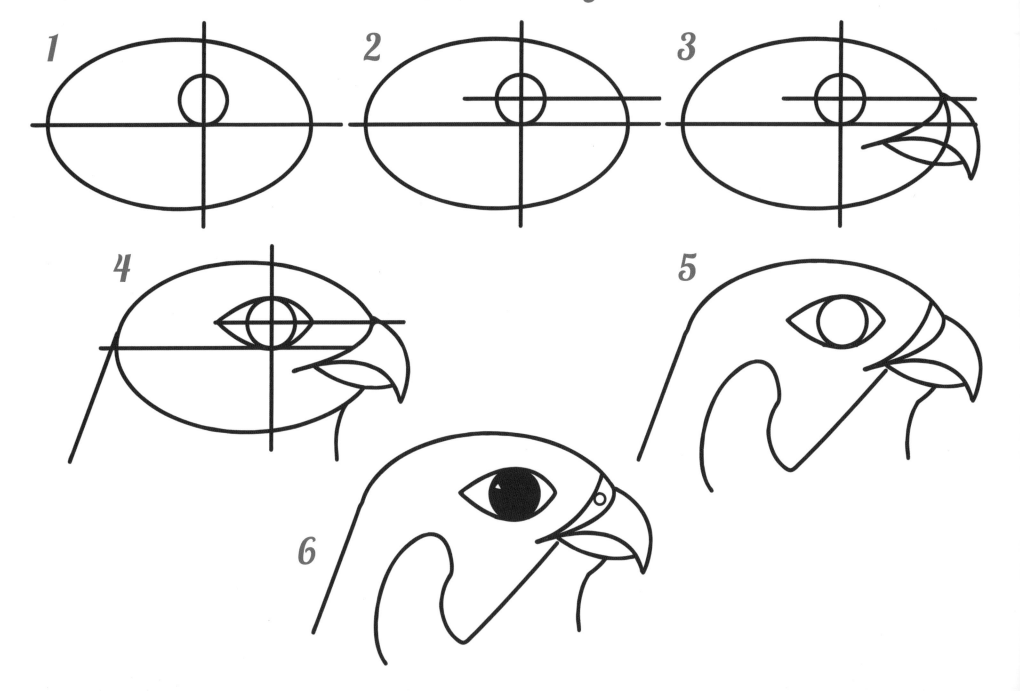

Draw The Stoop

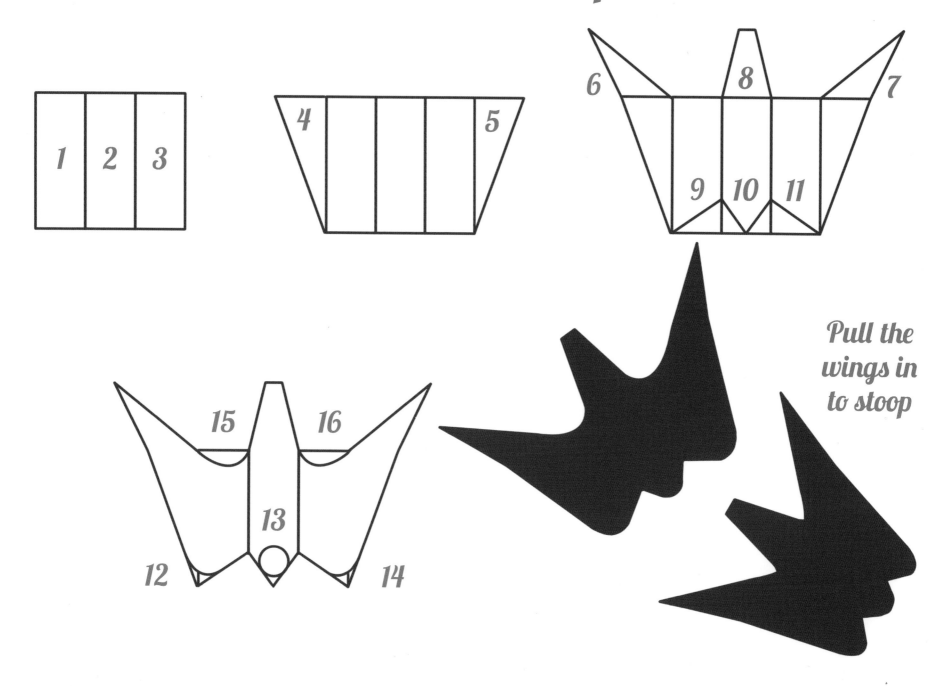

Pull the wings in to stoop

Top Gun Of The Sky began life as the poem The Fawley Falcon and is inspired by the rescue and rehabilitation of Gucci and Prada, two young Peregrine Falcons, by the Hawk Conservancy Trust.

As well as conducting rehabilitation and conservation work, the Hawk Conservancy Trust has an award-winning visitor centre near Andover in Hampshire where you can see Peregrines and over 150 other birds of prey, from owls to eagles!

Visit www.hawkconservancy.org for more information.

Publication of this book was made possible through the generous support of ExxonMobil's Fawley Refinery. The team at Fawley Refinery is committed to supporting conservation both on site and in the wider community. A portion of the proceeds from each book goes directly to the work of the Hawk Conservancy Trust.

HAWK CONSERVANCY TRUST

ExxonMobil
Supported by ExxonMobil at the Fawley Refinery